Test Book

EXPLORING THE UNIVERSE

Prentice Hall
Englewood Cliffs, New Jersey
Needham, Massachusetts

Test Book

PRENTICE HALL SCIENCE
Exploring the Universe

ISBN 0-13-987298-1

13 14 15   99 98 97 96

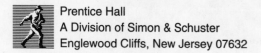
Prentice Hall
A Division of Simon & Schuster
Englewood Cliffs, New Jersey 07632

Contents

To the Teacher

This *Test Book* contains all the testing materials that accompany the student textbook. The testing materials are divided into three parts:

CHAPTER TEST

Every chapter in the student textbook has an accompanying Chapter Test. These tests are meant to test both factual recall and concept development. Each Chapter Test is divided into five sections. These sections are Multiple Choice, Completion, True or False, Using Science Skills, and Essay. An Answer Key for each Chapter Test is also included.

COMPUTER TEST BANK TEST

Every chapter in the student textbook has an accompanying Computer Test Bank Chapter Test. These tests are meant to test both factual recall and concept development. Each Computer Test Bank Test is divided into five sections. These sections are Multiple Choice, True or False, Completion, Using Science Skills, and Critical Thinking and Application. An Answer Key for each Test Bank Test is also included.

You may choose to copy the entire Computer Test Bank Chapter Test. A complete User's Guide is included in the disk package. Using your computer and the test disks, you can print out your own chapter test, quiz, midterm exam, or final exam, selecting questions from the Test Bank as well as adding your own. An Illustration Master for each visual question in the Test Bank Test is included after the questions. These Illustration Masters are to be used when you print out a test from your printer. An Answer Key for each test is also included.

The APPLE, IBM, and MAC disks for the ***Prentice Hall Science*** Computer Test Banks include questions from the Computer Test Bank for all 19 titles in the program.

For current prices and ordering information call your Customer Service Representative toll free 1-800-848-9500. Refer to the appropriate ISBN number below.

Item (ISBN #)	Description
0-13-987686-3	Apple 5 1/4-inch Program and Data Disks for the *Prentice Hall Science* Computer Test Bank (User's Guide included)
0-13-987702-9	IBM 5 1/4-inch Program and Data Disks for the *Prentice Hall Science* Computer Test Bank (User's Guide included)
0-13-986944-1	IBM 3 1/2-inch Program and Data Disks for the *Prentice Hall Science* Computer Test Bank (User's Guide included)
0-13-987694-4	MAC 3 1/2-inch Program and Data Disks for the *Prentice Hall Science* Computer Test Bank (User's Guide included)

PERFORMANCE-BASED TESTS

A set of Performance-Based Tests is included in this *Test Book*. Performance-Based Tests are designed to test a student's thinking and problem-solving abilities, and are not meant to be content dependent. Although the tests have been designed to be given when the student has completed the textbook, you may prefer to give individual tests after particular chapters in the textbook. If you like, you may incorporate some of the Performance-Based Tests into your Chapter Test.

Performance-Based Tests are given at workstations. All materials the student needs are placed at the workstation, along with the worksheets the student must fill out. Students must be told in advance the amount of time they will have at each workstation. Make sure students understand that they must leave the workstation exactly as they found it.

Contents

Chapter Test

CHAPTER 1 ■ Stars and Galaxies

MULTIPLE CHOICE

Write the letter of the correct answer on the line at the left.

_____ 1. A universe that expands and comes back together repeatedly is
   a. closed.
   b. open.
   c. subject to only one big bang.
   d. called an eternal universe.

_____ 2. Quasars are
   a. nebulae.
   b. close to Earth.
   c. pulsars.
   d. very distant.

_____ 3. The Large and Small Magellanic Clouds are examples of
   a. nebulae.
   b. irregular galaxies.
   c. spiral galaxies.
   d. elliptical galaxies.

_____ 4. The smallest stars are called
   a. main-sequence stars.
   b. protostars.
   c. white dwarfs.
   d. neutron stars.

_____ 5. The most common element in stars is
   a. helium.
   b. carbon.
   c. hydrogen.
   d. iron.

_____ 6. Which of the following is used to measure the distances to stars?
   a. parallax
   b. red-shift measurement
   c. a formula involving apparent magnitude and absolute magnitude
   d. all of these

_____ 7. A force that tends to pull together the matter in stars is
   a. gravity.
   b. nuclear fusion.
   c. expansion.
   d. nuclear fission.

_____ 8. Pulsating variable stars are
   a. binary stars.
   b. novas.
   c. pulsars.
   d. Cepheid variables.

_____ 9. Pulsars are
   a. neutron stars.
   b. white dwarfs.
   c. supergiants.
   d. novas.

_____ 10. A supernova is the explosion of a
   a. medium-sized star.
   b. massive star.
   c. protostar.
   d. nebula.

COMPLETION

Complete each statement on the line at the left.

_____ 1. The sun is located in a galaxy called the _____.

_____ 2. Algol is an example of a(an) _____.

_____ 3. Gemini, Leo, and Canis Major are examples of _____.

_____ 4. The largest stars are called _____.

_____ 5. A star's brightness as it appears from Earth is called _____.

TRUE OR FALSE

Determine whether each statement is true or false. If it is true, write T. If it is false, change the underlined word or words to make the statement true.

_____ _____ 1. A(An) <u>spectroscope</u> is an instrument used to break the light from stars into its colors.

_____ _____ 2. The spectrum of a star approaching Earth is shifted toward the <u>red</u> end of the spectrum.

_____ _____ 3. The apparent change in light wavelengths due to the motion of an object is called <u>parallax</u>.

_____ _____ 4. According to the <u>big bang theory</u>, all the matter and energy in the universe was once compressed into a single area.

_____ _____ 5. A diagram in which the absolute magnitude of stars is plotted against their average surface temperature is called a <u>Hertzsprung-Russell diagram</u>.

Name _____ Class _____ Date _____

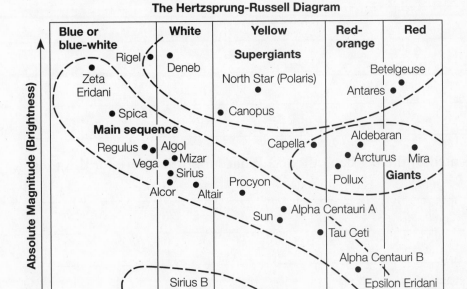

The Hertzsprung-Russell Diagram

1. What color is the star Deneb?_____

   What is its surface temperature? _____

   What type of star is Deneb? _____

2. Which star has the highest surface temperature? a. Sun b. Procyon c. Betelgeuse

   d. Sirius B _____

3. Which star is brightest? a. Sun b. Procyon c. Betelgeuse d. Sirius B _____

4. Which star is largest? a. Sun b. Procyon c. Betelgeuse d. Sirius B _____

5. Which star is smallest? a. Sun b. Procyon c. Betelgeuse d. Sirius B _____

6. What is the general relationship between surface temperature and brightness of main-

   sequence stars? _____

   _____

ESSAY

Write a brief paragraph discussing each of the following statements or questions.

1. Account for the blue shift and red shift of the spectrum of stars._____

_____

_____

_____

_____

_____

2. What is stated by the big bang theory? What support is there for this theory? _____

_____

_____

_____

_____

_____

3. Explain the difference between absolute magnitude and apparent magnitude. _____

_____

_____

_____

_____

_____

4. Compare and contrast the life cycles of a medium-sized star, a massive star, and a super-

nova star. _____

_____

_____

_____

_____

_____

_____

_____

Answer Key

MULTIPLE CHOICE

1. a 2. d 3. b 4. d 5. c 6. d 7. a 8. d 9. a 10. b

COMPLETION

1. Milky Way 2. eclipsing binary 3. constellations 4. supergiants 5. apparent magnitude

TRUE OR FALSE

1. T 2. F, blue 3. F, the Doppler effect 4. T 5. T

USING SCIENCE SKILLS

1. white; about 10,000°C; supergiant 2. d 3. c 4. c 5. d 6. As temperature increases, brightness increases.

ESSAY

1. Red shift occurs when the wavelength of light from a star appears longer than it really is. Red shift occurs for stars moving away from Earth. Blue shift occurs when the wavelength of light from a star appears shorter than it is. Blue shift occurs for stars moving toward Earth. The apparent change in wavelength is called the Doppler effect. 2. According to the big bang theory, all the matter and energy in the universe were once compressed into a small, hot, dense area. An enormous explosion occurred, and matter and energy moved outward rapidly. Background radiation that is uniform throughout the universe is evidence in favor of the big bang theory. The energy of this radiation is left over from the big bang. 3. Absolute magnitude is the actual brightness of a star. It depends on the amount of light the star gives off. Apparent magnitude is the brightness of a star as it is seen from Earth. It depends on both the amount of light the star gives off and the distance of the star from Earth. 4. All the stars begin as protostars formed from nebulae. All convert hydrogen to helium at first. Medium-sized stars then expand, their outer shells cool, and they become red giants. Their cores heat up and produce carbon. Finally they cool and collapse inward, forming white dwarfs that eventually become dead stars. Massive and supermassive stars turn into red giants that continue to heat up, producing iron. They then explode in supernovas, producing heavier elements. The cores of massive stars go on to contract into neutron stars. The cores of supermassive stars go on to contract into black holes.

Test Bank Test

CHAPTER 1 ■ Stars and Galaxies

MULTIPLE CHOICE

Write the letter of the answer that best completes each statement.

_____ 1. A band of colors formed when white light passes through a prism is called a
    a. lens.
    b. photograph.
    c. spectrum.
    d. ray.

_____ 2. Astronomers use optical telescopes to detect
    a. radio waves.
    b. infrared radiation.
    c. X-rays.
    d. visible light.

_____ 3. What characteristic of a star indicates whether the star is moving toward or away from Earth?
    a. size
    b. age
    c. roundness
    d. spectrum

_____ 4. Galaxies that are moving away from Earth have light spectra characteristic of
    a. a red shift.
    b. a blue shift.
    c. a black hole.
    d. the sun.

_____ 5. The attraction between galaxies, which are composed of huge amounts of matter, is due to
    a. changes in air pressure.
    b. light spectra patterns.
    c. gravity.
    d. temperature variations.

_____ 6. Evidence that supports the big bang theory of the origin of the universe includes the fact that galaxies
    a. are speeding away from the center of the universe.
    b. are collected at the center of the universe.
    c. exert a force on other galaxies in space.
    d. give off radiation.

_____ 7. The idea of an open universe leads one to believe that
    a. the big bang never took place.
    b. everything in the universe may eventually disappear.
    c. stars are free to move toward one another.
    d. galaxies are all moving toward the center of the universe.

_____ 8. Which of the following illustrates a blue shift?
    a. galaxy racing toward the edge of the universe
    b. an open universe
    c. an approaching star
    d. light from distant galaxies

_____ 9. The big bang theory is based on the assumption that
   a. our present universe is the result of the expansion of matter from a single point.
   b. once stars formed, matter moved toward the center of the universe.
   c. galaxies near the edge of our universe are moving toward the center of the universe.
   d. the center of our universe was originally cold and dense.

_____ 10. Which of the following most accurately explains why quasars are considered mysterious?
   a. They are closest to the center of the universe
   b. They give off light like stars
   c. Their light spectra show a blue shift
   d. They give off much more energy than several galaxies combined

_____ 11. How long does it take light from a quasar 6 billion light-years away to reach Earth?
   a. 6 minutes   c. 6 million years
   b. 6 years   d. 6 billion years

_____ 12. The main factor that shapes the life and eventual death of a star is its
   a. mass.   c. temperature.
   b. color.   d. diameter.

_____ 13. Globular star clusters differ from open clusters because the stars in globular clusters are
   a. arranged in a sphere.   c. arranged in a large, loosely organized group.
   b. dimmer in brightness.   d. eclipsing binaries.

_____ 14. According to astronomers, most stars are actually paired stars called
   a. nebulae.   c. galaxies.
   b. novas.   d. binaries.

_____ 15. Stars that suddenly increase in brightness and then get dim are identified as
   a. novas.   c quasars.
   b. nebulae.   d. galaxies.

_____ 16. A star that will live the longest has a starting mass that is
   a. extra large.   c. medium sized.
   b. small.   d. large.

_____ 17. Which of the following is *not* a constellation in our night sky?
   a. Orion   c. Rigel
   b. Gemini   d. Little Dipper

_____ 18. An example of a white dwarf star is
   a. Van Maanen's star.   c. Antares.
   b. the sun.   d. Polaris.

_____ 19. An astronomer determines the surface temperature of a star by its
   a. size.   c. brightness.
   b. color.   d. position in the sky.

_____ 20. What element makes up more than 60 percent of the mass of a typical star?
   a. nitrogen   c. neon
   b. carbon   d. hydrogen

_____ **21.** The color of a star is related to its
    a. size.   c. distance from Earth.
    b. temperature.   d. shape.

_____ **22.** Fusion within an aging red giant star causes
    a. the temperature in the core of the star to rise.
    b. helium atoms to fuse into hydrogen atoms.
    c. the outer hydrogen shell of the star to collapse.
    d. matter in the star to spread out so that the star becomes a massive star.

_____ **23.** Which of the following stars is least like the others in surface temperature?
    a. the sun   c. Spica
    b. Alpha Centauri A   d. Procyon

_____ **24.** The Hertzsprung-Russell diagram does not provide information about a star's
    a. distance from Earth.   c. surface temperature.
    b. color.   d. brightness.

_____ **25.** Parallax is a method used to determine a star's
    a. temperature.   c. composition.
    b. distance from Earth.   d. brightness.

_____ **26.** Black holes result from the death of
    a. protostars.   c. supermassive stars.
    b. medium-sized stars.   d. white dwarfs.

_____ **27.** Star distances from Earth of more than 100 light-years can be measured by
    a. brightness.   c. temperature.
    b. parallax.   d. a spectroscope.

_____ **28.** Magnitude refers to a star's
    a. color.   c. brightness.
    b. size.   d. distance from Earth.

_____ **29.** The outermost layer of the sun's atmosphere is the
    a. chromosphere.   c. corona.
    b. photosphere.   d. prominence.

_____ **30.** Which of the following is *not* a type of solar storm?
    a. corona   c. sunspot
    b. prominence   d. solar flare

TRUE OR FALSE

Determine whether each statement is true or false.

_____ **31.** All objects in our universe are moving.

_____ **32.** Long wavelengths are characteristic of blue and violet light.

_____ **33.** Astronomers agree that all of the galaxies are moving away from each other at the same speed.

_____ **34.** A closed universe will experience another big bang.

_____ 35. The word stellar means starlike.

_____ 36. Our sun is a star that belongs to a multiple star system.

_____ 37. Oxygen is the lightest element.

_____ 38. The hottest main-sequence stars shine with an orange or red light.

_____ 39. A planetary nebula forms when hydrogen gas surrounding a red giant star drifts away.

_____ 40. The sun is composed of gases and liquids.

COMPLETION

Fill in the word or number that best completes each statement.

_____ 41. Planet Earth is located in the _____ Galaxy.

_____ 42. A(An) _____ galaxy is shaped like a pinwheel.

_____ 43. The unit used to measure distances between celestial objects is the _____.

_____ 44. Arrange the following objects in order of decreasing size by placing the appropriate numbers on the line: (1) galaxy, (2) nebula, (3) Earth, (4) universe.

_____ 45. The galaxies closest to the Milky Way are the _____, which are irregular galaxies.

_____ 46. The Hercules cluster of stars is an example of a(an) _____ cluster.

_____ 47. _____ is the closest star (other than the sun) to Earth.

_____ 48. To a casual observer, stars appear as small points of _____ in the nighttime sky.

_____ 49. Arrange the following stars in order of size from the smallest to the largest: (1) sun-sized stars, (2) white dwarf stars, (3) neutron stars, (4) giant stars, (5) supergiant stars.

_____ 50. The _____ cycle of a star represents the various stages a star goes through from "birth" to "death."

_____ 51. Great heat given off during nuclear fusion in a nebula causes a(an) _____ to form.

_____ 52. A star shines with a _____ color when most of the hydrogen gas in the star has been converted into helium.

_____ 53. The _____ of a star is the main factor in shaping its life cycle.

_____ 54. The core of a very massive star is so hot that fusion continues until the heavy element _____ is formed.

_____ 55. The _____ Nebula formed from the supernova explosion of a dying star in AD 1054.

_____ **56.** Neutron stars that give off bursts of radio waves are called _____.

_____ **57.** In a(an) _____, light passes through a prism and is broken into a band of colors.

_____ **58.** The amount of light a star actually gives off is called its _____.

_____ **59.** Double star systems are called _____.

_____ **60.** The _____ is the innermost of the three layers of the sun's atmosphere.

USING SCIENCE SKILLS

Use the skills you have developed in the chapter to answer each question.

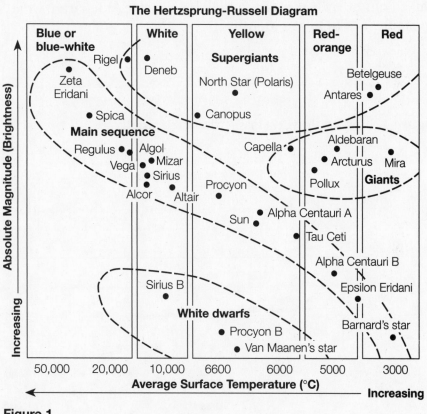

Figure 1

61. Using Figure 1, name a star that is very dim and red in color.

62. Using Figure 1, compare our sun to Alpha Centauri A in terms of brightness, color, and surface temperature.

63. Using Figure 1, describe the ways in which Barnard's star and Antares are alike.

64. Using Figure 1, name the stars that have surface temperatures above 10,000 degrees Celsius.

65. Using Figure 1, describe three features of the star Deneb.

66. If you walked out on a clear night to look for the star Aldebaran, what clues would you use from Figure 1 to help you identify it?

67. Using Figure 1, how would you classify the star Capella?

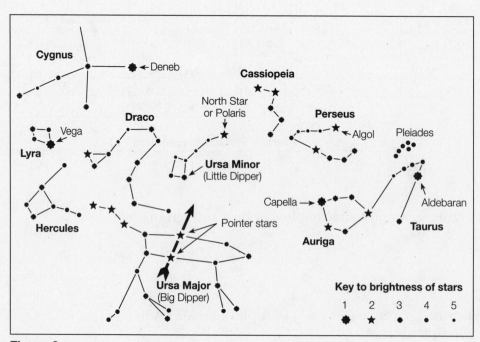

Figure 2

68. According to Figure 2, in what constellation are the pointer stars located?

69. According to Figure 2, how many stars have a brightness of 1?

70. According to Figure 2, how many stars in the constellation Cygnus have a brightness of 3?

71. According to Figure 2, in which constellation is the star Vega located?

72. Of the constellations shown in Figure 2, which contain stars with a brightness of 5?

73. Using Figure 2, compare the brightness of stars in Ursa Minor with those in Cassiopeia.

CRITICAL THINKING AND APPLICATION

Discuss each of the following in a brief paragraph.

74. Assuming you know how long a star takes to proceed from birth to its eventual death, what can you then infer about the star's mass when it first formed?

75. The big bang theory attempts to explain how the universe formed. Do you agree or disagree with this theory? Explain your answer.

76. The sun is a medium-sized star gliding through space in the Milky Way Galaxy. Explain why the sun does not fall into the center of the Milky Way.

77. Explain how a spectroscope provides information about stars millions of light-years away from Earth.

78. If an astronomer intends to analyze starlight from distant stars, would the geographic location of the observatory be an important factor?

79. The big bang theory provides one explanation for the formation of the universe. Using this theory, explain what the oldest objects in the universe would be and why.

80. Compare the basic features of spiral and elliptical galaxies.

81. Explain why Algol is a "winking" star.

82. What is the difference between a binary star and an eclipsing binary?

83. Compare apparent magnitude and absolute magnitude of stars.

The Hertzsprung-Russell Diagram

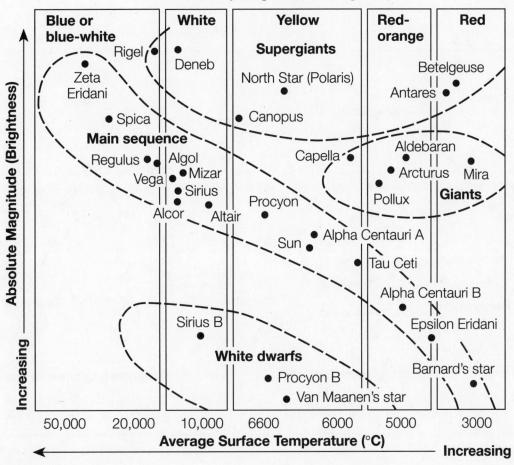

Figure 1

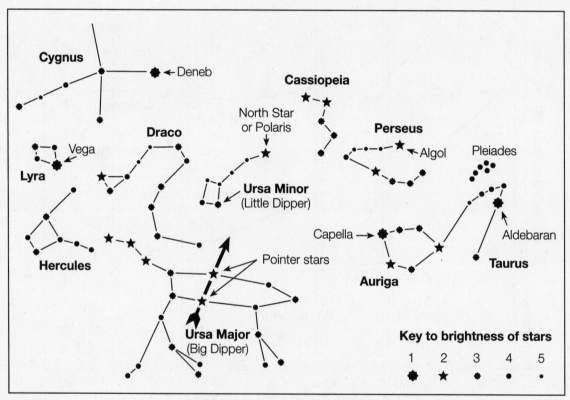

Figure 2

Test Bank Answer Key

1. c
2. d
3. d
4. a
5. c
6. a
7. b
8. c
9. a
10. d
11. d
12. a
13. a
14. d
15. a
16. b
17. c
18. a
19. b
20. d
21. b
22. a
23. c
24. a
25. b
26. c
27. b
28. c
29. c
30. a
31. T
32. F
33. F
34. T
35. T
36. F
37. F
38. F
39. T
40. F

41. Milky Way
42. spiral
43. light-year
44. 4, 1, 2, 3
45. Large and Small Magellanic Clouds
46. globular
47. Alpha Centauri
48. light
49. 3, 2, 1, 4, 5
50. life
51. protostar
52. red
53. mass
54. iron
55. Crab
56. pulsars
57. spectroscope
58. absolute magnitude
59. binary stars
60. photosphere
61. Barnard's star
62. Both stars are yellow in color but Alpha Centauri A is slightly brighter than our sun. Our sun is slightly hotter than Alpha Centauri A.
63. They both have about the same surface temperatures and color.
64. Algol, Regulus, Spica, Rigel, Zeta Eridani
65. Deneb is an extremely bright star, white in color, with an average surface temperature of 10,000 degrees Celsius.
66. Aldebaran is very bright and red-orange in color.
67. Capella is a bright yellow giant with a surface temperature of 6000 degrees Celsius.
68. Ursa Major (Big Dipper)
69. four stars
70. two stars
71. Lyra

72. Cygnus, Draco, Ursa Minor, Perseus, Taurus
73. Both constellations contain stars with brightnesses of 3 and 4, but Ursa Minor also has stars with a brightness of 5 and Cassiopeia does not.
74. A general assumption that can be made is that the larger the starting mass of a star, the shorter will be its life cycle. For example, for medium-sized stars, a star with a small mass will live about 100 billion years, while a star with a large mass will live only a few billion years. Thus, if you know how long a star lives, you can then infer how large its mass was when it first formed.
75. Student answers will vary. Accept all logical explanations.
76. The sun is not standing still in space but is revolving around the center of the Milky Way Galaxy. The gravitational forces of stars near the center of the galaxy pull the sun toward the center. The sun's inertia, however, causes it to travel in a straight line. The combination of gravity and inertia keeps the sun from falling into the center of the galaxy or from speeding off into space and leaving the galaxy.
77. Light captured from a distant star passes through the prism of a spectroscope and is broken down into the various colors that make up the light. The band of colors produced is called a spectrum. Every element present in the light source has a characteristic spectrum. The spectrum is like a bright-line fingerprint that enables astronomers to identify the basic makeup of the star. A shift in the spectral lines to either blue or red indicates the star is moving toward or away from us, respectively. The amount of shift also indicates how far from Earth the star is.
78. An observatory should be located where there is the least amount of atmospheric interference. Major cities have considerable air pollution and light interference, which add unnecessary and interfering data to the results. Locating the observatory great distances from a city and on top of a mountain eliminates both forms of interference to a major degree. The best location for an observatory is in a satellite in outer space. Here there is no interference from city lights and pollution.
79. Those objects that were the first to leave the center of the universe after the big bang took place would be the oldest. These objects are probably the quasars, which are located on the outermost edge of the universe.
80. Both types of galaxies contain enormous numbers of stars and have characteristic shapes. Elliptical galaxies are spherical to round to flat in appearance. Spiral galaxies exhibit streamers of stars emerging from a common center in a spiraling or swirling motion. The stars in elliptical galaxies are usually older stars.
81. Algol is really two stars that revolve around each other. Algol's companion star is much dimmer. When it passes in front of Algol, the light from Algol is blocked. Every three days, Algol dims to about one-third its normal brightness and thus appears to "wink."
82. Binary stars simply revolve around each other. But in eclipsing binary stars, one of the stars in the pair passes in front of the other, blocking out some of its light and making it appear to "wink," or dim and brighten repeatedly.
83. Apparent magnitude is a star's brightness as it appears from Earth. Absolute magnitude is the actual amount of light that a star gives off. The magnitude scale is based on apparent brightness. Stars can have the same absolute magnitudes but different apparent magnitudes because of their different distances from Earth.

Contents

Chapter Test

CHAPTER 2 ■ The Solar System

MULTIPLE CHOICE

Write the letter of the correct answer on the line at the left.

_____ **1.** The solar system includes
    a. the sun.   c. asteroids.
    b. the planets.   d. all of these

_____ **2.** The moons of planets are called
    a. asteroids.   c. satellites.
    b. comets.   d. protoplanets.

_____ **3.** A chunk of ice, dust, and gas from the Oort cloud that moves around the sun is called a(an)
    a. asteroid.   c. meteoroid.
    b. comet.   d. planet.

_____ **4.** The orbits of the planets are
    a. elliptical.   c. linear.
    b. circular.   d. completely irregular.

_____ **5.** The law that states that an object's motion will not change unless it is acted upon by an outside force is called the law of
    a. gravity.   c. inertia.
    b. elliptical motion.   d. force.

_____ **6.** A planet whose rotation is retrograde is
    a. Mercury.   c. Jupiter.
    b. Mars.   d. Venus.

_____ **7.** The planet that has a reddish surface and two moons is
    a. Mercury.   c. Jupiter.
    b. Mars.   d. Venus.

_____ **8.** The planet that seems to be tipped on its side is
    a. Uranus.   c. Jupiter.
    b. Neptune.   d. Pluto.

_____ **9.** Which of the following is a moon of Jupiter?
    a. Io   c. Phobos
    b. Titan   d. Triton

_____ **10.** Chunks of rock in a belt between the orbits of Mars and Jupiter are called
    a. asteroids.   c. meteors.
    b. comets.   d. meteorites.

COMPLETION

Complete each statement on the line at the left.

_____ 1. The theory that states that the solar system began as a huge cloud of dust and gas is called the _____.

_____ 2. An imaginary line about which a planet rotates is called its _____.

_____ 3. The movement of a planet around the sun is called _____.

_____ 4. The largest single structure in the solar system is a field around Jupiter that is called the _____.

_____ 5. The nucleus, coma, and tail are parts of a(an) _____.

TRUE OR FALSE

Determine whether each statement is true or false. If it is true, write T. If it is false, change the underlined word or words to make the statement true.

____ _____ 1. The time it takes a planet to turn once on its axis is called its period of <u>revolution</u>.

____ _____ 2. The large clumps that eventually became planets are called <u>protoplanets</u>.

____ _____ 3. There are <u>nine</u> known planets in our solar system.

____ _____ 4. The planet that has the most obvious ring system is <u>Mars</u>.

____ _____ 5. A solid, rocklike object that can enter Earth's atmosphere is called a <u>meteorite</u>.

USING SCIENCE SKILLS: Making Observations, Interpreting Illustrations

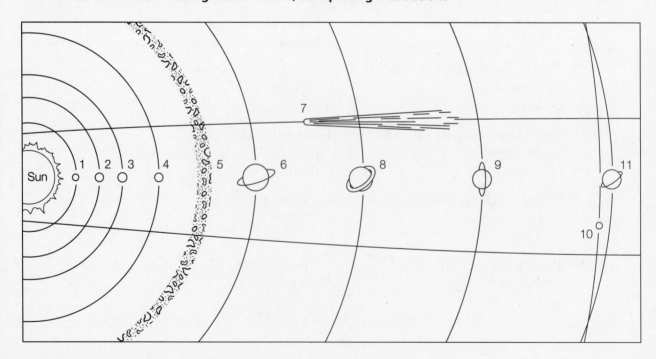

1. What is the name of object 1? _____

    2? _____

    4? _____

    6? _____

    8? _____

    9? _____

    What are these objects? _____

2. What object is labeled 10? _____

    11? _____

    Which is now closer to the sun? _____

3. What is located in the area labeled 5? _____

4. What is object 7? _____

    Where did it originate? _____

ESSAY

Write a brief paragraph discussing each of the following statements.

1. Describe the way in which the solar system was probably formed. _____

_____

_____

_____

_____

_____

2. Compare the formation of the inner planets and the outer planets. _____

_____

_____

_____

_____

_____

_____

3. Account for the curved orbits of planets. _____

_____

_____

_____

_____

_____

_____

4. Explain the difference between a meteoroid, meteor, and meteorite.

_____

_____

_____

_____

_____

_____

_____

Answer Key

MULTIPLE CHOICE

1. d 2. c 3. b 4. a 5. c 6. d 7. b 8. a 9. a 10. a

COMPLETION

1. nebular theory 2. axis 3. revolution 4. magnetosphere 5. comet

TRUE OR FALSE

1. F, rotation 2. T 3. T 4. F, Saturn 5. F, meteoroid

USING SCIENCE SKILLS

1. 1 Mercury; 2 Venus; 4 Mars; 6 Jupiter; 8 Saturn; 9 Uranus. Planets. 2. 10 Pluto; 11 Neptune. Pluto is now closer to the sun than is Neptune. Pluto will be farther from the sun in the future. 3. asteroids 4. Comet. It originated in the Oort cloud.

ESSAY

1. The solar system began as a nebula, or cloud of dust and gas. A supernova explosion of a nearby star disturbed the nebula and released elements that spread into it. Shock waves caused gases in the nebula to contract and to spin more and more rapidly. The nebula flattened into a disk at whose center a protosun formed. Some of the other circling matter clumped together to form proto-planets, which developed into planets. 2. Protoplanets near the sun became so hot that most of their lightweight gases, such as hydrogen and helium, boiled away, leaving these protoplanets as collections of metals and rocky materials. The protoplanets farther from the sun were less affected by the sun's heat. They retained their lightweight gases and grew to enormous sizes. 3. The planets, as moving objects, would, according to the law of inertia, move at constant speed and direction unless acted on by an outside force. The planets are also gravitationally attracted by the sun, which tends to pull them toward it. These two factors together account for the elliptical orbits. 4. Meteoroids are solid rocklike objects that revolve around the sun. When a meteoroid enters Earth's atmosphere, friction causes a bright gas streak of light. This glow of gases is called a meteor. The iron and/or stony material that hits Earth is called a meteorite.

Test Bank Test

CHAPTER 2 ■ The Solar System

MULTIPLE CHOICE

Write the letter of the answer that best completes each statement.

_____ **1.** In order to measure the diameter of our sun, which of the following units of measure would you use?
   a. kilogram   c. kilometer
   b. kiloliter   d. degree Celsius

_____ **2.** Which of the following planets is referred to as an inner planet of our solar system?
   a. Saturn   c. Jupiter
   b. Pluto   d. Mercury

_____ **3.** Data on the makeup of Martian soil were relayed back to Earth by
   a. Mariner 10.   c. Pioneer.
   b. Venera 1.   d. Viking.

_____ **4.** The solar system includes the
   a. sun and other stars.
   b. inner planets, Earth, and outer planets.
   c. inner planets, outer planets, asteroids, and moons.
   d. sun, its planets, and all other objects that revolve around the sun.

_____ **5.** Astronomers believe that our solar system began as a
   a. nebula.   c. neutron star.
   b. black hole.   d. white dwarf.

_____ **6.** Evidence today indicates that the age of our solar system is about
   a. 1 billion years. c. 5 billion years.
   b. 3 billion years. d. 7 billion years.

_____ **7.** The primary gases present when our solar system was formed were helium and
   a. oxygen.   c. methane.
   b. nitrogen.   d. hydrogen.

_____ **8.** Rocklike objects called asteroids are located in an orbit between Jupiter and
   a. Earth.   c. Saturn.
   b. Mars.   d. Venus.

_____ **9.** It is believed that the home of the comets is located
   a. between Saturn and Uranus.   c. between Mars and Jupiter.
   b. very near the sun.   d. near the outer edge of the solar system.

_____ **10.** Our sun, once known as a protosun, finally became a star when
   a. planetary gases in space contracted.
   b. a star near the vicinity of our forming sun exploded into a supernova.
   c. shock waves passing through space spread through a nearby nebula.
   d. hydrogen present in the protosun fused into helium atoms.

_____ **11.** Compared with a day on Earth, a day on Mercury is
     a. longer.   c. shorter.
     b. the same.   d. half as long.

_____ **12.** The most recent evidence about numerous craters and steep cliffs on Mercury has been obtained by
     a. optical telescopes.   c. the spectroscope.
     b. Pioneer.   d. Mariner 10.

_____ **13.** The period of Earth's rotation is equal to
     a. 365 days.   c. 24 hours.
     b. 29.8 kilometers per second.   d. 58 degrees Celsius.

_____ **14.** Which of the following properties makes Venus greatly different from Earth?
     a. mass   c. size
     b. rotation   d. density

_____ **15.** Two objects in our solar system that have active volcanoes are Earth and
     a. the moon.   c. Ganymede.
     b. Mercury.   d. Io.

_____ **16.** Which of the following is the most likely hypothesis as to why Mars once had water on its surface?
     a. Water vapor streamed into the Martian atmosphere from Jupiter and collected into seas
     b. Volcanoes deposited steam in the Martian atmosphere that formed into liquid water
     c. Vast quantities of water vapor were trapped by Martian gravity during the passage of a comet
     d. Earth had too much water vapor in its atmosphere, and huge amounts escaped to outer space and were captured by Mars

_____ **17.** Huge craters present on the surface of Mercury seem to indicate that
     a. large solid objects struck the surface of the planet.
     b. mountains once on the surface of the planet subsided below the surface.
     c. tremendous winds eroded the soil of the planet.
     d. explosions from the sun scarred the surface of the planet.

_____ **18.** Astronomers believe that comets are formed in
     a. the atmosphere of Europa.
     b. the region between Mars and Jupiter.
     c. a galaxy other than the Milky Way.
     d. the Oort cloud.

_____ **19.** Which of the following characteristics is unique in our solar system to the planet Uranus?
     a. rings around the planet   c. craters on the surface
     b. axis tilted sideways   d. more than ten moons

_____ **20.** From which planet could you obtain information about planetary rings?
     a. Mars   c. Mercury
     b. Venus   d. Neptune

_____ **21.** If Earth were to suddenly move closer to the sun, which of the following would occur?
     a. A year would be longer   c. A year would be shorter
     b. A day would be longer   d. A day would be shorter

_____ 22. Which of the following best defines the astronomical term comet?
  a. anything composed of dust and gas
  b. a cloud of dust and ice surrounding a common nucleus
  c. a gas and ice cloud traveling through space
  d. an object made of ice, dust, and gas speeding through space

_____ 23. A comet's tail continually points away from the sun because of the
  a. composition of the comet.
  b. solar wind blowing from the sun.
  c. length of the comet's orbit.
  d. temperature of the comet's core.

_____ 24. According to Johannes Kepler's theory, the planets of the solar system revolve around
  a. the sun.   c. the moon.
  b. the Earth.   d. each other.

_____ 25. The time it takes for a planet to make one complete trip around the sun is its period of
  a. rotation.   c. orbit.
  b. day.   d. revolution.

_____ 26. An entire day on Mercury is equal to about how many Earth-days?
  a. 127   c. 59
  b. 43   d. 88

_____ 27. Which of the following is *not* one of Jupiter's moons?
  a. Callisto   c. Ganymede
  b. Europa   d. Vesuvius

_____ 28. Temperatures on Mercury range from 427°C to –170°C mainly because of the planet's
  a. long period of rotation.   c. short period of rotation.
  b. long period of revolution. d. short period of revolution.

_____ 29. The idea that the solar system began in a vast gas cloud is called the
  a. heliocentric theory.   c. geocentric theory.
  b. nebular theory.   d. elliptical theory.

_____ 30. Smaller clumps of matter that formed around the planets are called
  a. protosuns.   c. moons.
  b. protoplanets.   d. asteroids.

TRUE OR FALSE

Determine whether each statement is true or false.

_____ 31. The word planet is derived from a Latin word meaning wanderer.

_____ 32. Orbits of planets are circular in shape.

_____ 33. The atmospheres of Earth and Mars are composed mostly of hydrogen and helium.

_____ **34.** Planets with very thin atmospheres do not store much heat from the sun at their surfaces.

_____ **35.** The polar icecaps of Mars are both composed mainly of frozen water.

_____ **36.** At one time in the past, Venus may have had huge bodies of water on its surface.

_____ **37.** Io is a moon that orbits Saturn in a regular path.

_____ **38.** "Shooting stars" that reach the surface of Earth are known as meteorites.

_____ **39.** The solar wind has no effect on comets while the comets are near the sun.

_____ **40.** An orbit is a path an object takes when moving around another object in space.

COMPLETION

Fill in the word or number that best completes each statement.

_____ **41.** Planets in our solar system follow an egg-shaped or _____ orbit as they travel through space.

_____ **42.** The closest planet to our sun is _____, which is covered with many _____ that dot the surface of the planet.

_____

_____ **43.** Mapping the planet Venus has already been done by _____, a space craft that relayed radar data back to Earth.

_____ **44.** Planets in our solar system have two kinds of motion called _____ and _____.

_____

_____ **45.** The planet _____ takes the longest time of any planet to complete one orbit around the sun.

_____ **46.** The only planet in our solar system that has its axis tilted sideways is _____.

_____ **47.** A year is the time it takes for a planet to make one _____ around the sun.

_____ **48.** A combination of _____ and _____ causes a planet to move in an elliptical orbit.

_____

_____ **49.** The planet that prominently displays the volcano Olympus Mons on its surface is _____.

_____ **50.** The _____ is the process by which heat is trapped beneath the thick clouds of a planet.

_____ **51.** The northern icecap of the planet _____ is made mostly of frozen water, and the southern icecap is made mostly of frozen _____.

_____ **52.** The two major gases in the atmosphere of Jupiter are _____ and helium.

_____ **53.** The four moons orbiting Jupiter that were discovered by Galileo include _____, _____, _____, and Callisto.

_____

_____

_____ **54.** The planet in our solar system that has the most moons is _____.

_____ **55.** It is now known that Saturn's spectacular rings are made up of _____.

_____ **56.** A thick atmosphere made of _____, helium, and _____ covers the planet Uranus.

_____

_____ **57.** Neptune is known to have five rings and _____ moons.

_____ **58.** A _____ is the stony material that strikes Earth from outer space.

_____ **59.** The most famous short-period comet to visit the center of the solar system is _____.

_____ **60.** The _____ contains about 99.8 percent of all the matter in the solar system.

USING SCIENCE SKILLS

Use the skills you have developed in the chapter to answer each question.

Planet	Average Distance From the Sun in km x 1,000,000	Orbital Velocity in km/sec
Mercury	0.6	47.8
Venus	1.1	35.0
Earth	1.5	29.8
Mars	2.3	24.2
Jupiter	7.8	13.1
Saturn	14.3	9.7
Uranus	28.7	6.8
Neptune	44.9	5.4
Pluto	58.9	4.7

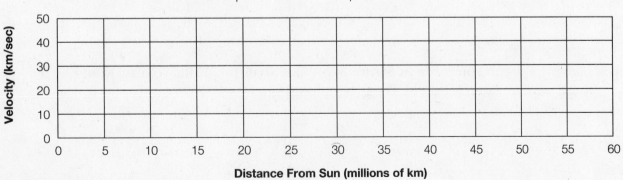

Figure 3

61. Plot the velocities and distances on the graph shown in Figure 3. The horizontal axis stands for the distance from the sun, and the vertical axis stands for velocity. Connect your plotted points with a smooth line.

62. From the velocities given in Figure 3, calculate the average velocity of the planets in our solar system.

63. Between which two planets on the graph you made in Figure 3 will the average velocity occur?

64. Describe the appearance of the line formed by the points on the graph you made in Figure 3.

65. What does the graph you made in Figure 3 tell about orbital velocity as distance increases?

66. Between which two planets on the graph you made in Figure 3 is the distance the greatest?

67. Between which two planets on the graph you made in Figure 3 is there the greatest change in orbital velocity?

68. Using the graph you made in Figure 3, predict what the orbital velocity would be if there were a planet located halfway between Jupiter and Saturn.

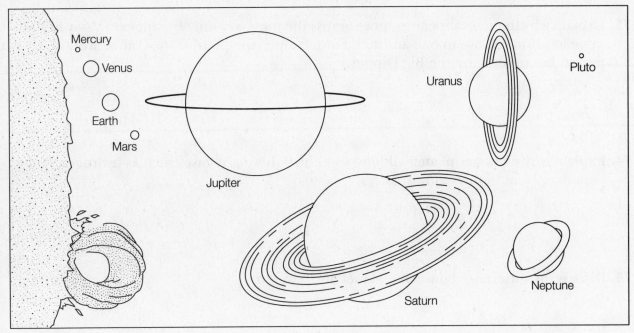

Figure 4

69. Using a metric ruler and a piece of paper, measure the diameter of Earth in Figure 4.

70. Using Figure 4, determine about how many Earth diameters will fit into the diameter of Uranus. (Use paper and pencil if needed.)

71. Using Figure 4 and a metric ruler, determine the diameter of Neptune.

72. Using Figure 4, how many times bigger in diameter is Jupiter than Neptune?

CRITICAL THINKING AND APPLICATION

Discuss each of the following in a brief paragraph.

73. Explain why the stars appear to move across the night sky but also appear to stay in the same location relative to one another. For example, the pointer stars move around in the sky but never leave the Big Dipper.

74. Explain why the outer planets did not lose the lightweight gases such as hydrogen and helium present in their atmospheres.

75. Discuss the difference between a planet and a moon.

76. Defend this statement: "There would not be any life on Earth if the sun did not shine."

77. Predict what would happen to the planets if the sun were to disappear from the center of our solar system.

78. Design an experiment to prove that the sun rotates on its axis.

79. Arrange the following orbits by assigning each a number from 1 (smallest) to 5 (largest).

_____   Pluto around the sun

_____   our moon around Earth

_____   sun around the center of the Milky Way

_____   Saturn around the sun

_____   Earth around the sun

80. If Mercury's inertia suddenly became zero, what would happen to Mercury?

81. Image that you are a traveler to the planets Jupiter, Saturn, Uranus, and Neptune. While on each planet you look back at the sun to see how big it appears. Below are the sizes of the sun as it appears to you from each planet. Write the planet name under the correct sun size.

10 mm diameter 5 mm diameter   15 mm diameter   7 mm diameter

a._____ b. _____ c. _____ d. _____

82. The sun, like the planets, rotates on its axis. However, some parts of the sun take longer to rotate than others. Suggest a possible explanation for this.

Planet	Average Distance From the Sun in km x 1,000,000	Orbital Velocity in km/sec
Mercury	0.6	47.8
Venus	1.1	35.0
Earth	1.5	29.8
Mars	2.3	24.2
Jupiter	7.8	13.1
Saturn	14.3	9.7
Uranus	28.7	6.8
Neptune	44.9	5.4
Pluto	58.9	4.7

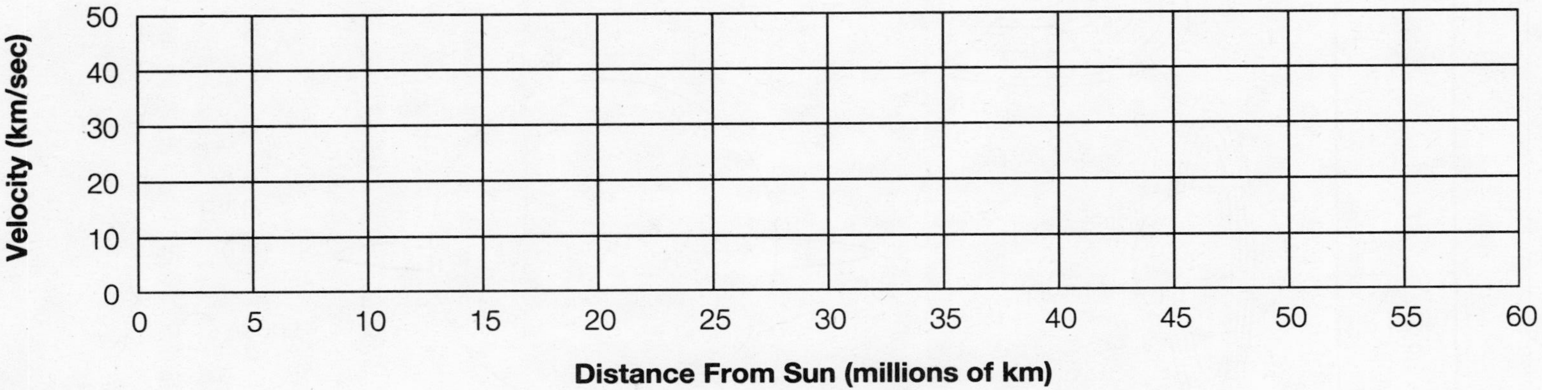

Distance From Sun (millions of km)

Velocity (km/sec)

Figure 3

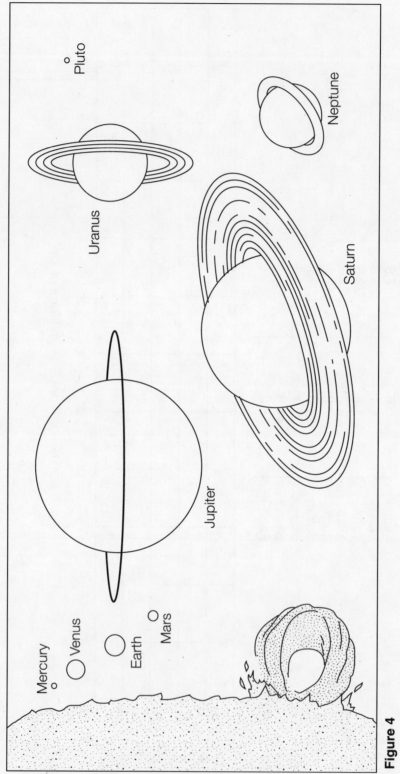

Figure 4

Test Bank Answer Key

1. c
2. d
3. d
4. d
5. a
6. c
7. d
8. b
9. d
10. d
11. a
12. d
13. c
14. b

15. d
16. b
17. a
18. d
19. b
20. d
21. c
22. d
23. b
24. a
25. d
26. c
27. d
28. a

29. b
30. c
31. T
32. F
33. F
34. T
35. F
36. T
37. F
38. T
39. F
40. T

41. elliptical
42. Mercury, craters
43. Pioneer Venus Orbiter
44. revolution, rotation
45. Pluto
46. Uranus
47. revolution
48. gravity, inertia
49. Mars
50. greenhouse effect
51. Mars, carbon dioxide
52. hydrogen
53. Io, Europa, Ganymede
54. Saturn
55. icy particles
56. hydrogen, methane
57. eight
58. meteorite
59. Halley's comet
60. sun
61. Check students' graphs.
62. 19.61 km/sec
63. Mars and Jupiter
64. The resulting line begins with a sharp downward curve from left to right, tapering off to an almost straight line on the right.
65. It decreases.
66. Uranus and Neptune
67. Mercury and Venus
68. approximately 11 km/sec
69. 0.5 cm
70. 3.5
71. about 1.5 cm
72. about three times

73. The movement of stars across the sky is due to the rotation of Earth on its axis. The dome of the heavens appears to move above us. The stars in the Big Dipper are so far away from us that they appear to be motionless.

74. The outer planets are a tremendous distance away from the sun, thus they are much cooler than the inner planets. This fact prevented the lightweight gases from being boiled away by the intense heat of the sun.

75. The basic differences between planets and moons are their masses and their motions. Planets revolve around the sun, while moons revolve around a planet. Planets are not as massive as the sun but are more massive than moons. Both planets and moons are composed of clumps of metals and rocky materials.

76. All life on Earth requires energy to live and grow. The source of all energy on this planet comes from the sun. If the sun suddenly ceased to shine, this planet would quickly become very cold, lifeless, and dark.

77. The planets are held in their orbits by the force of gravity that exists between the sun and each planet. With the sun gone, there would be no gravity to hold the planets in orbit, and they would go off into space in the direction that inertia would send them. In addition, all planets would get extremely cold and dark due to the absence of heat and light from the sun.

78. Student answers may vary. A good experiment includes the indirect observation of sunspots by use of binoculars and white paper. Arrange to observe and record sightings of sunspots at regular intervals, then compare sightings to confirm that sunspots move across the face of the sun. If the sunspots move from right to left, left to right, or from top to bottom, then the axis of the sun will be perpendicular to the direction of sunspot movement.

79. 4, 1, 5, 3, 2

80. Mercury would be drawn into the sun.

81. a. Saturn b. Neptune c. Jupiter d. Uranus

82. The sun is made of different gases, which move at different speeds.

Contents

CHAPTER 3 ■ Earth and Its Moon

CHAPTER 3

Chapter Test

CHAPTER 3 ■ Earth and Its Moon

MULTIPLE CHOICE

Write the letter of the correct answer on the line at the left.

_____ 1. The moon's dark, smooth areas discovered by Galileo are called
    a. maria.   c. umbras.
    b. highlands.   d. rilles.

_____ 2. The Earth rotates
    a. around the sun.   c. from east to west.
    b. around the moon.   d. from west to east.

_____ 3. When the South Pole is tilted toward the sun, it is
    a. summer in both hemispheres.
    b. winter in both hemispheres.
    c. summer in the Northern Hemisphere and winter in the Southern
       Hemisphere.
    d. winter in the Northern Hemisphere and summer in the Southern
       Hemisphere.

_____ 4. A doughnut-shaped region that traps particles from the solar wind is a(an)
    a. umbra.   c. Van Allen belt.
    b. apogee.   d. penumbra.

_____ 5. The distance between the Earth and the moon is roughly
    a. 38.4 km.   c. 3840 km.
    b. 384 km.   d. 384,000 km.

_____ 6. The moon was probably formed
    a. long before Earth.   c. long after Earth.
    b. at the same time as Earth.   d. before the sun.

_____ 7. The phase of the moon that occurs just after the waxing-crescent and just before
    the waxing-gibbous phase is the
    a. first quarter.   c. new moon.
    b. full moon.   d. last quarter.

_____ 8. The completely dark inner area of the shadow of the Earth or moon is called the
    a. umbra.   c. partial eclipse.
    b. penumbra.   d. total eclipse.

_____ 9. Tides are caused mainly by
    a. wind.   c. the gravity of the moon.
    b. magnetic fields.   d. the gravity of the sun.

_____ 10. The period of the moon's revolution equals
    a. the period of its rotation.   c. twice the period of its rotation.
    b. half the period of its rotation.   d. 29 ½ times the period of its rotation.

COMPLETION

Complete each statement on the line at the left.

_____ **1.** The two halves of the Earth are called _____.

_____ **2.** A time at which day and night are of equal length all over the Earth is called a(an) _____.

_____ **3.** The Earth's magnetic field is called the _____.

_____ **4.** The point of the moon's orbit farthest from the Earth is called the _____.

_____ **5.** Tides that occur when the moon is in its first- and last-quarter phases are called _____.

TRUE OR FALSE

Determine whether each statement is true or false. If it is true, write T. If it is false, change the underlined word or words to make the statement true.

_____ _____ **1.** The gases that surround the Earth make up the <u>hydrosphere</u>.

_____ _____ **2.** One revolution of the Earth takes one <u>day</u>.

_____ _____ **3.** The time at which the Northern Hemisphere has its longest day and shortest night is called the <u>summer solstice</u>.

_____ _____ **4.** Temperatures on the moon <u>vary widely</u>.

_____ _____ **5.** When a part of the Earth passes into the moon's shadow, a <u>lunar</u> eclipse occurs.

USING SCIENCE SKILLS: Applying Concepts, Interpreting Illustrations

1. What is this event called? _____

2. What is the name for the region of the moon's shadow labeled A? _____

What is the name for the region labeled B? _____

3. What is occurring at region 1 of the Earth's surface? _____

At region 2? _____

At region 3? _____

At region 4? _____

At region 5? _____

4. How would the event that is occurring at region 1 differ if the Earth were farther from

the moon? Why? _____

_____

_____

_____

_____

_____

_____

ESSAY

Write a brief paragraph discussing each of the following statements or questions.

1. Explain what causes the seasons to occur. _____

_____

_____

_____

_____

_____

_____

_____

_____

2. Based on the moon's rotation and atmosphere, describe and account for its temperature conditions. _____

_____

_____

_____

_____

_____

3. Account for the occurrence of tides, for low and high tides, and for spring and neap tides.

_____

_____

_____

_____

_____

4. How is it possible for the sun to affect the Earth's magnetic field?_____

_____

_____

_____

_____

_____

_____

Answer Key

MULTIPLE CHOICE

1. a **2.** d **3.** d **4.** c **5.** d **6.** b **7.** a **8.** a **9.** c **10.** a

COMPLETION

1. hemispheres **2.** equinox **3.** magnetosphere **4.** apogee **5.** neap tides

TRUE OR FALSE

1. F, atmosphere **2.** F, year **3.** T **4.** T **5.** F, solar

USING SCIENCE SKILLS

1. a solar eclipse **2.** umbra; penumbra **3.** partial eclipse (of the sun); total eclipse; partial eclipse; full daylight; night **4.** The total eclipse would affect a smaller area of the Earth's surface because the umbra, or area in complete shadow, would be smaller. If the Earth were far enough away, there would be no area in the umbra and no total eclipse.

ESSAY.

1. The Earth's axis is tilted. As the Earth revolves around the sun, a given hemisphere is tilted first toward it, then neither toward it nor away from it, then away from it, and then neither toward it nor away from it. These four situations correspond, respectively, to summer, autumn, winter, and spring in that hemisphere. The heating of the Earth depends on the amount and directness of light from the sun, which depends on the tilting. **2.** Temperatures range greatly, from very high on the light side to very cold on the dark side. This is because the same side of the moon is lighted for a relatively long period by the sun since the moon's rotation is so slow. Also, there is no atmosphere to transfer heat. The latter also accounts for low temperatures in the shadowed areas. **3.** Tides occur mostly because of the moon's gravitational pull, which causes a significant outward bulge of the water on the sides of the Earth nearest to and farthest from the moon. In those two areas, the tides are high. In the areas between the bulges, tides are low. The sun's gravitational pull also has an effect on the oceans. When the sun and moon are in line (when the moon is new or full) spring tides, or especially high high tides, occur because the sun and moon act together. When the sun and moon are at right angles relative to the Earth (when the moon is in first or last quarter) their gravitational effects partly cancel each other and the result is neap tides, which are relatively low high tides. **4.** When the solar wind strikes the magnetosphere, it reshapes the magnetosphere as the Earth rotates on its axis, forming a long tail on the side facing away from the sun.

Test Bank Test

CHAPTER 3 ■ Earth and Its Moon

MULTIPLE CHOICE

Write the letter of the answer that best completes each statement.

_____ 1. The Explorer satellites launched in the late 1950s discovered two
   a. moons around the planet Uranus.
   b. unusually large craters in the state of Arizona.
   c. doughnut-shaped regions 2000 km above the surface of the Earth.
   d. active volcanic fissures in the Mid-Atlantic Ridge.

_____ 2. The distance from the Earth to the moon is about
   a. 384 km.   c. 38,400 km.
   b. 3840 km.   d. 384,000 km.

_____ 3. The Earth is divided into how many hemispheres?
   a. one   c. three
   b. two   d. four

_____ 4. The imaginary line that encircles the Earth midway between the North Pole and the South Pole is the
   a. equinox.   c. solstice.
   b. ocean shoreline.   d. equator.

_____ 5. The number of days it takes the moon to pass from the full-moon phase to the new-moon phase is
   a. 7 days.   c. 29.5 days.
   b. 14.75 days.   d. 31 days.

_____ 6. In mid-July, days would be the shortest in
   a. the Arctic.   c. Africa.
   b. the United States.   d. the Antarctic.

_____ 7. As seen looking down on the Earth from above the North Pole, the Earth is rotating
   a. clockwise.
   b. from the Northern to the Southern Hemisphere.
   c. counterclockwise.
   d. from the South Pole to the North Pole.

_____ 8. If the sun appears to rise in the east, then the Earth must be turning toward the
   a. south.   c. north.
   b. west.   d. east.

_____ 9. The Earth's magnetosphere is constantly being reshaped by the
   a. North Pole.   c. moon.
   b. aurora.   d. solar wind.

_____ **10.** The reason that the length of our days and nights changes is the
     a. axis of the Earth is straight up and down.
     b. Earth rotates from east to west.
     c. axis of the Earth is tilted.
     d. axis of the sun is tilted.

_____ **11.** How many times does Earth rotate in a month?
     a. 7 times   c. 30 times
     b. 15 times   d. 48 times

_____ **12.** The Earth will be one-fourth of its way around the sun in
     a. 30 days.   c. 182.5 days.
     b. 91 days.   d. 365 days.

_____ **13.** After the summer solstice occurs, the sun
     a. appears to move lower in the sky each succeeding day.
     b. appears to move slower across the sky each succeeding day.
     c. appears to move toward the North Pole each succeeding day.
     d. appears to move higher in the sky each succeeding day.

_____ **14.** The longest day of the year occurs at the
     a. vernal equinox.   c. autumnal equinox.
     b. summer solstice.   d. winter solstice.

_____ **15.** The reason the sun appears to set in the west is that
     a. the Earth turns away from the sun.
     b. the sun is revolving around the Earth.
     c. the Earth is rotating from east to west.
     d. the sun is rotating on its axis.

_____ **16.** The Earth's diameter is about 12,756 km. If the moon's diameter is about one-fourth that of the Earth, the moon's diameter is about
     a. 1594 km.   c. 6952 km.
     b. 3476 km.   d. 10,428 km.

_____ **17.** The Van Allen radiation belts were detected by instruments onboard the satellite
     a. Voyager.   c. Viking.
     b. Pioneer.   d. Explorer.

_____ **18.** Samples returned to the Earth reveal that the oldest moon rocks are
     a. about the same age as Earth rocks.
     b. twice as old as Earth rocks.
     c. younger than Earth rocks.
     d. three times as old as Earth rocks.

_____ **19.** There is no weather on the moon because
     a. there is too much sun.
     b. there is no atmosphere.
     c. one side of the moon is always without sunlight.
     d. there are only moderate traces of water present.

_____ **20.** At perigee in its orbit, the moon is
     a. closest to the sun.   c. nearest the Earth.
     b. farthest from the Earth.   d. farthest from the sun.

_____ **21.** When viewed against the background of the stars in our sky, the moon
    a. moves westward across the sky.
    b. remains stationary in the sky.
    c. rises in the west.
    d. moves eastward across the sky.

_____ **22.** When compared with the period of rotation of the Earth, the period of rotation of the moon is
    a. longer than the rotation of the Earth.
    b. no longer than 21.3 days.
    c. equal to the rotation of the Earth.
    d. shorter than the rotation of the Earth.

_____ **23.** The waxing-crescent moon occurs directly before the
    a. new moon.   c. full moon.
    b. waning-gibbous moon.   d. first-quarter moon.

_____ **24.** The "northern lights" is another name for the
    a. aurora borealis.   c. Van Allen belt.
    b. lunar eclipse.   d. penumbra.

_____ **25.** People in the umbra cast by the moon will see a(an)
    a. partial lunar eclipse.   c. total lunar eclipse.
    b. partial solar eclipse.   d. total solar eclipse.

_____ **26.** The new moon occurs directly before the
    a. crescent moon.   c. full moon.
    b. gibbous moon.   d. first-quarter moon.

_____ **27.** One complete rotation of Earth on its axis is equal to one
    a. hour.   c. year.
    b. day.   d. season.

_____ **28.** One complete revolution of Earth around the sun is equal to one
    a. hour.   c. year.
    b. day.   d. season.

_____ **29.** Earth has four seasons due to its
    a. rotation.   c. magnetism.
    b. hydrosphere.   d. tilted axis and revolution.

_____ **30.** The phases of the moon are caused by
    a. Earth revolving around the moon.   c. the moon revolving around Earth.
    b. Earth revolving around the sun.   d. the moon revolving around the sun.

TRUE OR FALSE

Determine whether each statement is true or false.

_____ **31.** The Earth has a diameter of 12,756 km.

_____ **32.** As seen from above the North Pole, the Earth rotates in a counterclockwise direction.

_____ 33. In the Northern Hemisphere, the longest day of the year occurs at the winter solstice.

_____ 34. The elements iron and nickel make up the Earth's core.

_____ 35. The moon has never had water present on its surface.

_____ 36. The rotation of the moon on its axis occurs once every 12 hours.

_____ 37. During the new-moon phase, the moon is not visible in the nighttime sky.

_____ 38. A solar eclipse occurs when the Earth comes between the sun and the moon.

_____ 39. Neap tides can occur when there is a new moon.

_____ 40. Earth is the only planet that has seasons.

COMPLETION

Fill in the word or number that best completes each statement.

_____ 41. The Earth rotates on its axis once every _____ hours.

_____ 42. Long days and short nights occur when the Earth's _____ points toward the sun.

_____ 43. On the day of the _____, the length of day and night are equal everywhere on the Earth.

_____ 44. The Van Allen radiation belts keep deadly rays of the _____ from reaching the Earth.

_____ 45. Long valleys called _____ are evidence that the moon might once have had active volcanoes.

_____ 46. The point of the moon's orbit when it is closest to the Earth is known as _____.

_____ 47. When the moon passes through the umbra of the Earth's shadow, a _____ eclipse occurs.

_____ 48. The moon's gravitational pull on the Earth causes _____, which are seen as the rise and fall of the ocean waters near shore.

_____ 49. _____ tides occur when the sun and moon line up with the Earth.

_____ 50. There are two high tides and two low tides every _____ hours on the Earth.

_____ 51. When the moon and sun are at right angles to the Earth, the shorelines experience _____ tides.

_____ 52. An imaginary line known as the _____ extends through the Earth from the North Pole to the South Pole.

_____ 53. The vernal equinox marks the beginning of _____.

_____ 54. The seasons of the year are caused by the _____ of the Earth's axis.

_____ **55.** Since the pull of gravity on the moon is less than the pull of gravity on the Earth, a person on Earth would weigh _____ than on the moon.

_____ **56.** The dark smooth areas on the surface of the moon are called _____, which means seas.

_____ **57.** The _____ is a great magnetic field that surrounds the Earth and extends far out into space.

_____ **58.** The time the Earth takes to complete one revolution around the sun is called a(an) _____.

_____ **59.** The tall mountain ranges on the moon are called _____.

_____ **60.** The point of the moon's orbit when it is farthest from the Earth is called the _____.

USING SCIENCE SKILLS

Use the skills you have developed in the chapter to answer each question.

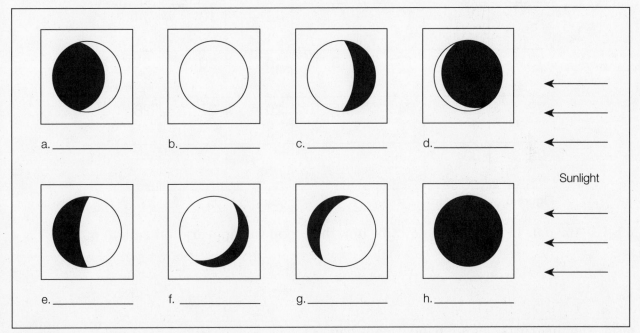

a._____ b._____ c._____ d._____

Sunlight

e._____ f._____ g._____ h._____

Figure 5

61. Using Figure 5, begin with the new moon as number 1 and arrange the moon phases in the proper order as they occur during the month.

62. Examine Figure 5. How long does it take for this entire cycle to occur?

63. Observe Figure 5. Why does this cycle occur?

64. Look at Figure 5. What happens when the cycle is finished?

JUNE						
Sun.	Mon.	Tue.	Wed.	Thur.	Fri.	Sat.
1	2	3	4	5	6	7 New moon
8	9	10	11	12	13	14
15	16	17	18	19	20	21 Full moon
22	23	24	25	26	27	28
29	30					

Figure 6

65. Use the data in Figure 6 to describe how the moon will appear on the night of June 7.

66. Using the data in Figure 6, how many days will have to pass from June 7 until you can see the next full moon?

67. Use Figure 6 to predict what day in June the first-quarter moon should be visible.

68. Use Figure 6 to describe what the moon should look like on the night of Wednesday, June 18. Name this phase.

69. Look at Figure 6. The month prior to June was May, and it had 31 days. On what date and day in May did the full moon last occur? Explain how you arrived at your answer.

70. From the June calendar in Figure 6, predict when the new moon will occur in the month of July.

71. Use Figure 6 to describe what the moon should look like when you go out at night on Saturday, June 28. What phase of the moon will you be observing on this night?

72. Using Figure 6, determine on what night in June the waning-crescent moon will be visible.

CRITICAL THINKING AND APPLICATION

Discuss each of the following in a brief paragraph.

73. Except for clouds, air pollution, and other natural phenomena, explain why we do not see a full moon each night of the month.

74. How is it possible that the sun and moon can have the same apparent size when you observe them in the sky?

75. Why is it that on December 21 each year, South America usually experiences hot days and North America usually has cold days?

76. Explain why daylight hours increase as we go from spring to summer.

77. Predict what would happen if the Earth's axis were no longer tilted at 23.5 degrees.

78. Is the surface of the moon entirely dark during a new moon? Explain.

79. Why do people living in the Arctic region of the Earth have 24 hours of sunlight with the beginning of the summer solstice?

80. The speed of the Earth's rotation at the equator is 1600 km/hr. Suppose you stand on the equator and a friend stands on the North Pole. Are you both rotating at the same speed? Explain.

81. Calculate how many kilometers a person will travel in one day if he or she stands on the equator while the Earth rotates beneath. Show your work. (The speed of the Earth = 1600 km/hr.)

82. Explain how a lunar eclipse differs from a solar eclipse.

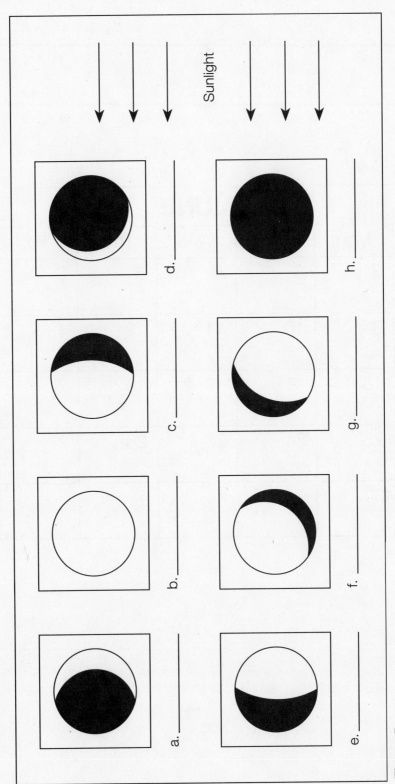

Figure 5

JUNE						
Sun.	Mon.	Tue.	Wed.	Thur.	Fri.	Sat.
1	2	3	4	5	6	7 New moon
8	9	10	11	12	13	14
15	16	17	18	19	20	21 Full moon
22	23	24	25	26	27	28
29	30					

Figure 6

Test Bank Answer Key

1. c
2. d
3. b
4. d
5. b
6. d
7. c
8. d
9. d
10. c
11. c
12. b
13. a
14. b

15. a
16. b
17. d
18. a
19. b
20. c
21. d
22. a
23. d
24. a
25. d
26. a
27. b
28. c

29. d
30. c
31. T
32. T
33. F
34. T
35. T
36. F
37. T
38. F
39. F
40. F

41. 24
42. axis
43. equinox
44. sun
45. rilles
46. perigee
47. total
48. tides
49. Spring
50. 24
51. neap
52. axis
53. spring
54. tilt
55. more
56. maria
57. magnetosphere
58. year
59. highlands
60. apogee
61. a. 2; b. 5; c. 7; d. 8; e. 3; f. 6; g. 4; h. 1
62. 29 ½ days
63. The moon revolves around the Earth.
64. The cycle starts over again.
65. You will not be able to see the moon as it will be a new moon. During the new moon, no sunlight is reflected from the moon's surface for you to see. The moon should be totally dark.
66. 14 days
67. Saturday, June 14
68. The moon should be midway between the first quarter and the full moon, and it should appear three-fourths lighted on the right side. This phase is the waxing-gibbous moon.
69. Saturday, May 24, was the occurrence of the last full moon. The moon makes one full cycle roughly every 28 days.
70. Saturday, July 5

71. On Saturday night, June 28, you will see the moon with the left side lighted and the right side dark. This is the last-quarter phase of the moon.

72. The night of June 3, or halfway between May 31 and June 7. (Answers may vary from June 2, 3, or 4.)

73. We do not always see a full moon because the moon is moving in its orbit around the Earth. As it orbits the Earth, more or less of the moon's surface appears lighted to an observer on Earth. When the Earth is between the sun and the moon, the entire lighted half of the moon, or a full moon, is visible.

74. Even though the sun is larger, it is many more times farther away from the Earth than the moon. As a result, both the sun and moon can appear to your eye to be about the same size.

75. The reason is due to the tilt of the Earth on its axis. On December 21, the Southern Hemisphere is tilted toward the sun, causing South America to have much sun and hot days. The Northern Hemisphere is tilted away from the sun, giving North America less sun and cold days.

76. Daylight hours increase because of the tilt of the Earth on its axis. As the Earth revolves around the sun from winter to summer, the tilt of the Earth causes more of the Northern Hemisphere to be exposed to the sun, causing the days to get longer each day.

77. The tilt of the Earth on its axis, along with its revolution around the sun, causes us to have four different seasons each year. If the axis were not tilted, neither hemisphere would get more light during part of the year. Rather, both hemispheres would receive equal amounts of sunlight at all times of the year, and we would no longer have seasons. This would affect the cycles of living things on the Earth as well as weather cycles.

78. No. The moon is not entirely dark. The side facing the Earth is dark because no sunlight strikes it. However, since the moon is a sphere, its far side is in full sunlight because it is exposed to the sun. We cannot see the far side of the moon from the Earth.

79. During the summer, the North Pole of the Earth is tilted more toward the sun, causing daylight to occur 24 hours each day.

80. No. Standing at the equator, you are traveling at the same speed as the Earth. However, as you go north from the equator, the distance that you travel in one rotation is less. Thus, your friend at the North Pole travels a very small distance for the same period of time, so his or her speed is much less than yours at the equator.

81. Speed of Earth = 1600 km/hr × 24 hr/day = 38,400 km/day

82. During a lunar eclipse, the Earth is directly in line between the sun and the moon, causing the moon to pass through the Earth's shadow. During a solar eclipse, the moon is directly in line between the sun and Earth, casting a shadow upon the Earth.

Contents

Performance-Based Assessment Rubrics

The Performance-Based Tests that follow provide you with an opportunity to evaluate both process skills and student understanding. Unlike methods of assessment that test factual recall, Performance-Based Tests demonstrate students' ability to *think logically*, utilize their *knowledge base, organize* their thoughts, and *perform basic skills* inherent to science and everyday life. Because students are not being tested on factual recall, it is important to keep in mind when scoring Performance-Based Tests that a logical and well-thought out answer can be scored just as high as the scientifically "correct" answer. Additional information on the theory behind performance-based assessment, as well as other forms of assessment such as portfolio assessment and oral reports, can be found on pages 76-77 in your Teacher's Desk Reference.

All of the Performance-Based Tests in the Prentice-Hall Science Learning System include one or more assessment objectives among the Teacher's Notes for each test. Using these objectives as the basis for evaluating skill development, the following assessment rubrics have been developed to assist you in your scoring. The rubrics allow for a range of student responses.

■ OUTSTANDING: RATING = 5

Student gives complete responses to all questions; provides a logical explanation for each response; completes all diagrams or data tables; uses descriptive terms accurately; completes the task; and demonstrates an understanding of the basic objectives.

■ COMPETENT: RATING = 4

Student gives complete responses to most questions, but is unable to provide a logical rationale for some answers; completes most diagrams or data tables; uses descriptive terms accurately; and demonstrates an understanding of the basic objectives.

■ SATISFACTORY: RATING = 3

Student gives incomplete answers to some questions and has a vague or limited rationale for answers; does not complete all diagrams or data tables; uses descriptive terms, but not always clearly or accurately; and demonstrates only a general understanding of the basic objectives.

■ UNSATISFACTORY: RATING = 2

Student provides very little response to most questions without any logical rationale for answers; does not complete most diagrams or data tables; does not use descriptive language; and does not exhibit an understanding of the basic objectives.

■ NO ATTEMPT: RATING = 1

Performance-Based Test

Test 1 A Tour of the Universe

Vacation trips around the universe have finally become a reality thanks to the invention of a faster-than-light starship drive early in the twenty-third century. However, tourists seem to be a little slow in taking advantage of the many sightseeing possibilities. As the newest member of a well-known advertising agency, you have been put in charge of the "Wonders of the Universe" account. If you can create a brilliant advertising campaign, it could make your career!

Check to make sure you have

1. large sheet of paper
2. colored pencils

Now you are ready to start.

Before you start writing your advertising copy, briefly summarize the important facts you know about the universe and its structure.

_____

_____

_____

_____

_____

_____

_____

_____

Now write a short, catchy advertisement for the "Wonders of the Universe" tour company. Illustrate your ad with drawings of a few of the interesting objects tourists might see during their trip through the universe.

_____

_____

_____

_____

DID YOU KNOW?

Travel through the universe has been a dream of science fiction writers and film makers for many years. It has also been very profitable. In only six months, the extremely popular film "E.T.: The Extra-Terrestrial" earned $322 million. The last film in the "Star Wars" trilogy, "Return of the Jedi," holds the record for single-day earnings: $8,440,105. Maybe you should consider switching from advertising to film making, as did director Ridley Scott ("Alien").

Performance-Based Test 1: A Tour of the Universe
Teacher Notes

MATERIALS

large sheet of paper
colored pencils

PREPARATION

No preparation is necessary.

OBJECTIVE

Students will design an advertising campaign for trips around the universe, thus demonstrating their understanding of the structure of the universe and the life cycle of stars.

REFERENCE

Chapter 1, Stars and Galaxies

Performance-Based Test

Test 2 Do-It-Yourself Planetarium

You have just returned from a visit to the local science center. You found many of the hands-on exhibits really interesting, especially the model planetarium showing the interactions among the sun, the Earth, and the moon. Wouldn't it be great if you could make something similar in your own home?

Check to make sure you have

1. desk lamp
2. ball about 8 cm in diameter
3. ring stand and ring

Now you are ready to start.

Set up the equipment to represent the sun and the moon so that the sun is shining on the moon. Does this arrangement accurately reflect what happens in nature? How do you know?

_____

_____

_____

_____

_____

_____

Stand behind the ball representing the moon so that you are facing the lamp. What do you notice about the ball?

_____

_____

_____

_____

_____

_____

_____

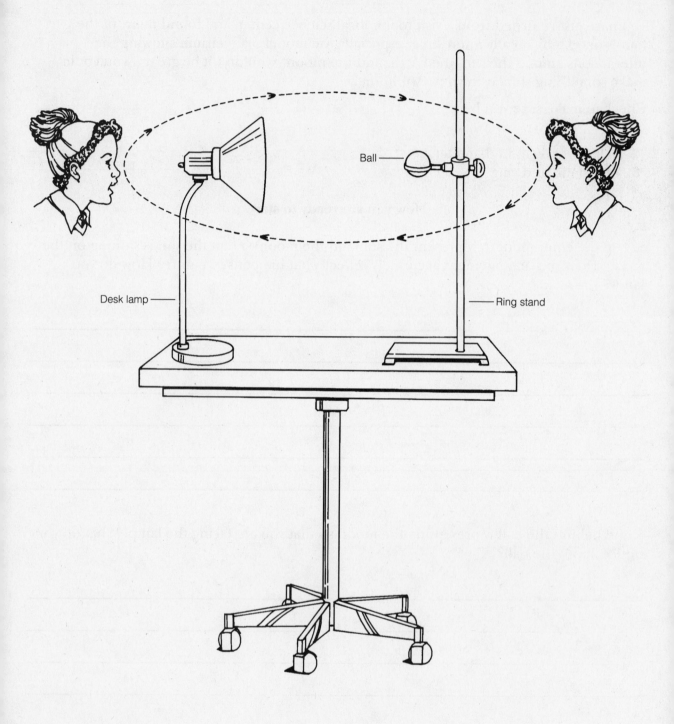

Ball

Desk lamp

Ring stand

Sketch your setup and indicate where you were standing. Draw the ball as it appears from your position.

From where you are standing behind the ball, walk 45° to the left and again draw the ball as it appears from your new position. Repeat this procedure two more times.

Now stand next to the lamp and repeat the procedure.

Look at the drawings you have made. Describe how your drawings are related to the changing appearance of the moon in the sky.

_____

_____

_____

_____

_____

Return to your original position behind the ball and draw what you see.

If you were to use this demonstration as an exhibit representing the relative positions of the sun, the Earth, and the moon, you would have to point out that it is slightly misleading. Why?

_____

_____

_____

_____

DID YOU KNOW?

We tend to think that most of what we know about the moon is fairly recent, dating from the Apollo moon landings of the 1970s. In fact, many ancient people had quite sophisticated knowledge about the moon. Here are some facts about the moon and the people who discovered them.

Lunar eclipses recorded ....Mesopotamians (about 2200 BC)

Lunar eclipses predicted...Babylonians (about 500 BC)

Moonlight is reflected sunlight ....Anaxagoras, Greek philosopher (about 459 BC)

Lunar eclipses show Earth is round.....................Aristotle, Greek philosopher (about 335 BC)

Distance from Earth to moon ....Aristarchus, Greek astronomer (about 280 BC)

Period of moon's revolution ....Hipparchus, Greek astronomer (about 150 BC)

Effect of moon and sun on tides ....Posidonius, Syrian philosopher (about 74 BC)

Performance-Based Test 2: Do-It-Yourself Planetarium
Teacher Notes

MATERIALS

desk lamp
ball, 8 cm in diameter
ring stand and ring

PREPARATION

Set up the equipment in an area that is not brightly lit so that the light from the lamp will be seen more easily.

OBJECTIVE

Using a lamp as a light source to represent the sun and a ball to represent the moon, students will observe the lighted ball from different angles. They will relate what they see to the phases of the moon and record their observations on paper.

REFERENCE

Chapter 3, Earth and Its Moon

Performance-Based Test

Test 3 Flame Tests

You are part of a team that will be classifying newly discovered stars based on the elements they contain. To do this, you will have to be able to identify the elements in the spectra of the stars. In order to prepare yourself for this task, you have decided to practice by matching solutions of different metals to the colors they produce in a flame test.

Check to make sure you have

1. Bunsen burner
2. 7 test tubes with different solutions
3. 1 test tube of hydrochloric acid
4. test-tube rack
5. safety goggles
6. wire loop
7. sheet identifying the different solutions

Now you are ready to start.

Put on your safety goggles. After each flame test, clean the wire loop by dipping it into the hydrochloric acid. Be sure to place the wire loop directly into the Bunsen burner flame to completely burn off the solution during each test. Prepare a data table to record your observations. When you are finished, identify the metal in each solution based on its color.

DID YOU KNOW?

Forensic scientists, or scientists who use their scientific knowledge to investigate crimes, are often asked to identify unknown substances removed from the scene of a crime. Flame tests are commonly used for this purpose.

Performance-Based Test 3: Flame Tests
Teacher Notes

MATERIALS

0.5 M solutions of
    A: calcium chloride
    B: lead (II) nitrate
    C: copper (II) sulfate
    D: potassium nitrate
    E: iron (II) sulfate
    F: barium chloride
    G: sodium chloride
4 M hydrochloric acid
Bunsen burner
8 test tubes
test-tube rack
safety goggles
wire loop
sheet listing the solutions in each test tube

PREPARATION

Identify each test tube by letter as shown. Each tube should contain 5 mL of solution. The eighth test tube should contain hydrochloric acid for cleaning the wire loop and must be clearly marked. Make sure students are wearing safety goggles.

OBJECTIVE

Students will demonstrate their ability to make accurate observations. They will use their observations to identify the metals in the unknown solutions.

REFERENCE

Chapter 1, Stars and Galaxies